Coloring Book
Gustave Baumann

Artist Gustave Baumann (American, b. Germany, 1881–1971) immigrated with his family to the United States from Germany when he was ten years old. At the age of sixteen he began full-time work in a commercial engraving house and took night classes in drawing at the Art Institute of Chicago to, in his words, "get a little closer to art." Baumann began work at an advertising studio and by 1903 had opened his own studio.

As soon as he had saved one thousand dollars from the new business, Baumann gave one half of the earnings to his mother and used the other half to travel to Munich to enroll in the School of Arts and Crafts located there. At the time, Munich printmakers were producing bold, innovative designs, which so deeply impressed Baumann that they influenced his work throughout his life. In rural Indiana, New York, New England, and the Southwest (where he lived for fifty years), he produced work that portrayed the spirit of his surroundings with respect and deep affection.

You'll find 22 of Gustave Baumann's artworks in this coloring book. They are shown as small pictures on the inside front and back covers. When you color the line drawings, you could choose to copy the originals, or you might prefer to create your own color combinations. We've left the last page of this coloring book blank so that you can draw and color a picture of your own. Will it be a landscape, a still life, or something wholly from your imagination?

New Mexico Museum of Art

Pomegranate Kids®

All artworks are by Gustave Baumann (American, b. Germany, 1881–1971).

1. *Point Lobos*, 1936. Color woodcut, 20.3 x 20.3 cm (8 x 8 in.). Collection of the New Mexico Museum of Art. Museum purchase with funds raised by the School of American Research, 1952. Photograph by Blair Clark. © Ann Baumann / New Mexico Museum of Art.

2. *Harden Hollow*, 1927. Color woodcut, 22.9 x 27.9 cm (9 x 11 in.). Collection of the New Mexico Museum of Art. Museum purchase with funds raised by the School of American Research, 1952. Photograph by Blair Clark. © Ann Baumann / New Mexico Museum of Art.

3. *El Santo*, 1919. Color woodcut, 22.9 x 27.9 cm (9 x 11 in.). Collection of the New Mexico Museum of Art. Museum purchase with funds raised by the School of American Research, 1952. Photograph by Blair Clark. © Ann Baumann / New Mexico Museum of Art.

4. *Marigolds*, 1929. Color woodcut, 32.4 x 32.4 cm (12¾ x 12¾ in.). Collection of the New Mexico Museum of Art. Museum purchase with funds raised by the School of American Research, 1952. Photograph by Blair Clark. © Ann Baumann / New Mexico Museum of Art.

5. *Tom A-Hunting*, 1917. Color woodcut, 27.9 x 33.7 cm (11 x 13¼ in.). Collection of the New Mexico Museum of Art. Museum purchase with funds raised by the School of American Research, 1952. Photograph by Blair Clark. © Ann Baumann / New Mexico Museum of Art.

6. *All the Year Round—January*, 1912. Color woodcut, 20.3 x 16.5 cm (8 x 6½ in.). Collection of the New Mexico Museum of Art. Museum purchase with funds raised by the School of American Research, 1952. Photograph by Blair Clark. © Ann Baumann / New Mexico Museum of Art.

7. *Zinnias*, c. 1915. Gouache, 31.8 x 34.3 cm (12½ x 13½ in.). Collection of the New Mexico Museum of Art. Gift of Jane H. Baumann, 1978. Photograph by Blair Clark. © Ann Baumann / New Mexico Museum of Art.

8. *The Bishop's Apricot*, 1924. Color woodcut, 15.2 x 19.4 cm (6 x 7⅝ in.). Collection of the New Mexico Museum of Art. Museum purchase with funds raised by the School of American Research, 1952. Photograph by Blair Clark. © Ann Baumann / New Mexico Museum of Art.

9. *San (Santo) Domingo Pueblo*, 1924. Color woodcut, 18.4 x 15.2 cm (7¼ x 6 in.). Collection of the New Mexico Museum of Art. Museum purchase with funds raised by the School of American Research, 1952. Photograph by Blair Clark. © Ann Baumann / New Mexico Museum of Art.

10. *Grandma Battin's Garden*, 1927. Color woodcut, 31.1 x 33.3 cm (12¼ x 13⅛ in.). Collection of the New Mexico Museum of Art. Museum purchase with funds raised by the School of American Research, 1952. Photograph by Blair Clark. © Ann Baumann / New Mexico Museum of Art.

11. *Idle Fleet*, 1917 (subsequent edition, 1931). Color woodcut, 24.1 x 27.9 cm (9½ x 11 in.). Collection of the New Mexico Museum of Art. Museum purchase with funds raised by the School of American Research, 1952. Photograph by Blair Clark. © Ann Baumann / New Mexico Museum of Art.

12. *All the Year Round—April*, 1912. Color woodcut, 20.3 x 16.5 cm (8 x 6½ in.). Collection of the New Mexico Museum of Art. Museum purchase with funds raised by the School of American Research, 1952. Photograph by Blair Clark. © Ann Baumann / New Mexico Museum of Art.

13. *Estes Park*, 1930. Gouache on paper, 26.7 x 23.5 cm (10½ x 9¼ in.). Photograph by Ron Chamberlain. © Ann Baumann / New Mexico Museum of Art.

14. *Corn Dance—Santa Clara*, 1924. Color woodcut, 15.2 x 19.1 cm (6 x 7½ in.). Collection of the New Mexico Museum of Art. Museum purchase with funds raised by the School of American Research, 1952. Photograph by Blair Clark. © Ann Baumann / New Mexico Museum of Art.

15. *Summer Clouds*, 1925. Color woodcut, 27.3 x 24.4 cm (10¾ x 9⅝ in.). Collection of the New Mexico Museum of Art. Museum purchase with funds raised by the School of American Research, 1952. Photograph by Blair Clark. © Ann Baumann / New Mexico Museum of Art.

16. *From Hillside Gardens*, 1941. Color woodcut, 31.8 x 31.8 cm (12½ x 12½ in.). Collection of the New Mexico Museum of Art. Museum purchase with funds raised by the School of American Research, 1952. Photograph by Blair Clark. © Ann Baumann / New Mexico Museum of Art.

17. *Summer Rain*, 1926. Color woodcut, 23.5 x 27.9 cm (9¼ x 11 in.). Collection of the New Mexico Museum of Art. Museum purchase with funds raised by the School of American Research, 1952. Photograph by Blair Clark. © Ann Baumann / New Mexico Museum of Art.

18. *Cholla and Sahuaro (Saguaro)*, 1928. Color woodcut, 32.4 x 32.4 cm (12¾ x 12¾ in.). Collection of the New Mexico Museum of Art. Museum purchase with funds raised by the School of American Research, 1952. Photograph by Blair Clark. © Ann Baumann / New Mexico Museum of Art.

19. *Nashville, Indiana*, 1913. Gouache on paper, 22.9 x 26.7 cm (9 x 10½ in.). Photograph by Ron Chamberlain. © Ann Baumann / New Mexico Museum of Art.

20. *Morning in Mexico*, 1934. Color woodcut, 30.5 x 33 cm (12 x 13 in.). Collection of the New Mexico Museum of Art. Museum purchase with funds raised by the School of American Research, 1952. Photograph by Blair Clark. © Ann Baumann / New Mexico Museum of Art.

21. *Pines—Grand Cañon*, 1920. Color woodcut, 32.7 x 32.7 cm (12⅞ x 12⅞ in.). Collection of the New Mexico Museum of Art. Museum purchase with funds raised by the School of American Research, 1952. Photograph by Blair Clark. © Ann Baumann / New Mexico Museum of Art.

22. *My Garden*, 1924. Color woodcut, 15.2 x 19.1 cm (6 x 7½ in.). Collection of the New Mexico Museum of Art. Museum purchase with funds raised by the School of American Research, 1952. Photograph by Blair Clark. © Ann Baumann / New Mexico Museum of Art.

Pomegranate Communications, Inc.
Box 808022, Petaluma CA 94975
800 227 1428   www.pomegranate.com

© 2011 Ann Baumann / New Mexico Museum of Art

Catalog No. CB132

Designed and rendered by Oky Sulistio

Printed in Korea, Fall 2010

20 19 18 17 16 15 14 13 12 11   10 9 8 7 6 5 4 3 2 1

Pomegranate Europe Ltd.
Unit 1, Heathcote Business Centre, Hurlbutt Road
Warwick, Warwickshire CV34 6TD, UK
[+44] 0 1926 430111
sales@pomeurope.co.uk

This product is in compliance with the Consumer Product Safety Improvement Act of 2008 (CPSIA). A General Conformity Certificate concerning Pomegranate's compliance with the CPSIA is available on our website at www.pomegranate.com, or by request at 800 227 1428.

For additional CPSIA-required tracking details, contact Pomegranate at 800 227 1428.

1. *Point Lobos*

2. Harden Hollow

3. El Santo

4. Marigolds

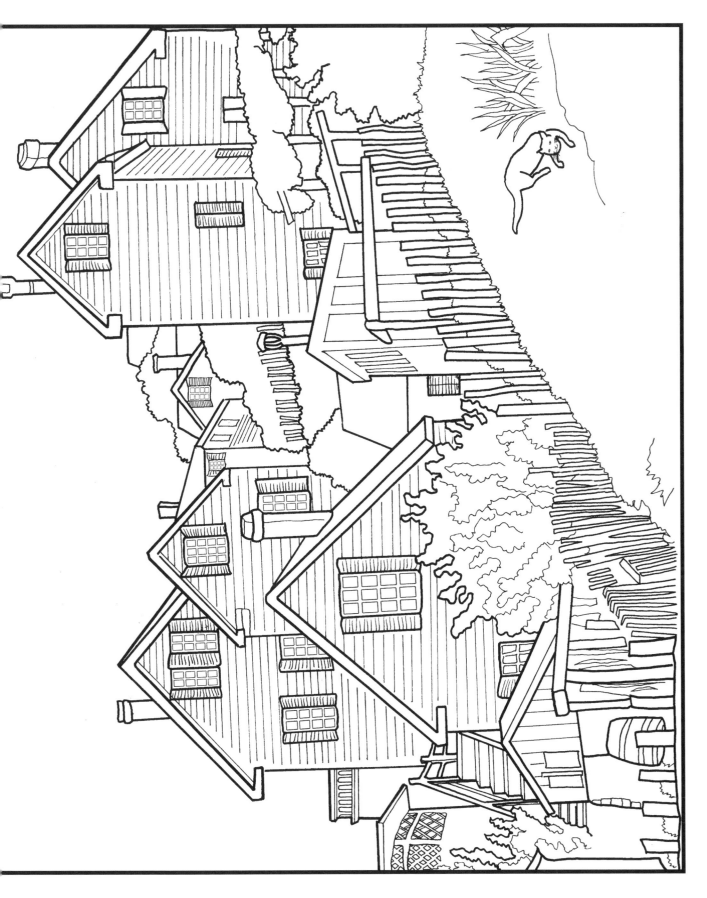

5. Tom A-Hunting

6. *All the Year Round—January*

7. Zinnias

8. The Bishop's Apricot

9. San (Santo) Domingo Pueblo

10. *Grandma Battin's Garden*

11. *Idle Fleet*

12. All the Year Round—April

13. *Estes Park*

14. Corn Dance—Santa Clara

15. *Summer Clouds*

16. *From Hillside Gardens*

17. Summer Rain

18. *Cholla and Sahuaro (Saguaro)*

19. Nashville, Indiana

20. *Morning in Mexico*

21. Pines—Grand Cañon

22. My Garden

Draw and color your own picture here!